Back of the Net

John Goodwin

Published in association with
The Basic Skills Agency

Hodder & Stoughton

Acknowledgements
Cover: Stuart Williams
Illustrations: Joan Corlass

Orders; please contact Bookpoint Ltd, 39 Milton Park, Abingdon, Oxon OX14
4TD. Telephone: (44) 01235 400414, Fax: (44) 01235 400454. Lines are open
from 9.00–6.00, Monday to Saturday, with a 24 hour message answering service.
Email address: orders@bookpoint.co.uk

British Library Cataloguing in Publication Data
A catalogue record for this title is available from the British Library

ISBN 0 340 77470 3

First published 2000
Impression number 10 9 8 7 6 5 4 3 2 1
Year   2005 2004 2003 2002 2001 2000

Copyright © 2000 John Goodwin

Typeset by GreenGate Publishing Services, Tonbridge, Kent.
Printed in Great Britain for Hodder and Stoughton Educational, a division of
Hodder Headline Plc, 338 Euston Road, London NW1 3BH, by Atheneum
Press, Gateshead, Tyne & Wear

Back of the Net

Contents

1

The Semi-Final

We ran on to the pitch.
Only the game mattered now.
This was the big one. The cup semi-final.
We had to win. It was as simple as that.
We owed it to ourselves.
We owed it to our fans.
'City ... City ... City,' they chanted.
I could still remember the words of our coach:
'It's all about goals today.
We have to turn in our best. Play like a team.
Work for each other.'

The warm-up time flashed by so fast.
The teams moved into position.
City in blue. Rovers in black and white.
Everything went quiet. It was silent.
Then the whistle blew. We were on our way.
The game was there for the winning.

Straight away Rovers broke into attack.
A long high kick upfield.
Their number nine raced after the ball.
Feet sprinted fast.
They barely seemed to touch the ground.
The ball bounced into a space.
Our defence was nowhere.
There was only our goalie to beat.
Number nine had control of the ball.
With a few swift touches the ball sped on.
The goal was getting closer and closer.
A shot for goal was on.
Still the number nine advanced.

Smack!

The ball rose in the air like a bird.
It was bang on target.
In goal Chalky seemed to have it covered.
She kept quite still.
Her eyes were on the ball.
Still it rose in the air. Then it fell.
Like a stone falling from the sky.
It was falling right on goal.
Chalky was ready.
She'd positioned herself in the right spot.

Suddenly the ball swerved.
It must have been the wind that caught it.
Chalky was in the wrong spot.
The ball was zooming towards
the corner of the net.
It had 1–0 written all over it.
Nothing could stop it.

Chalky flung herself sideways.
Somehow the tips of her fingers
touched the ball.
It skidded off her fingers
and over the touchline.
The ref's whistle blew for a corner.

'Wake up City,' shouted our coach. 'Wake up.'
It was the shock we needed.
Chalky caught the corner kick in both hands.
She held the ball tight.
'Emma … Emma …' she shouted.

She threw the ball out.
It went straight to Emma.
We were on our way.
Now we would show them how we could play.
It was class stuff.
Emma took three paces and then made
the through ball to Samita.
Samita passed it straight back to Emma.
A quick one two. Too quick for their defence.

'Mollie ...' shouted Emma.

I looked up to see a neat pass
heading my way.
I gathered the ball and made progress.
The goalie came off her line.
She came right towards me.
'Chip it. Chip it, Mollie.
Over her head and into the back of the net,'
shouted Emma.

I steadied myself. The empty goal was clear.
We could be 1–0 up. Back went my foot.
Now it was our turn
to see the ball fly like a bird.
But the bird was too high.
It kept rising and rising.
It zoomed way over the top of the goal.
I'd wasted a great chance.
The match finished a 0–0 draw.
We'd have to have a replay.

2

Gary

After the match I went
to the fish and chip shop.
I was so hungry I could have eaten
the biggest sack of chips in the world.
I know I was supposed to be in training
but I was starving.
Bad news.
There was a huge queue
outside the shop.
It went right along the pavement.
I'd just have to stand and wait in the queue.

I was trying to forget how much
my belly hurt when this lad gave me a chip.
He and his mates had been
at the front of the queue.

'Cheers,' I said eating his chip.
'Go on, have a few more,'
he said with a grin on his face.
'You'll have none left,' I said.
'I'm not that hungry
and you look starving,' he said.

I helped myself to a couple more of his chips
and looked at the lad.
He had deep blue eyes,
a shaved head and a real nice smile.
'Come on Gary,' shouted his mates.

He went off up the road with his mates.
I stood in that queue for ages
and all I could think about was his smile.
I walked back through the park
eating my own chips when I saw him again.
He was sitting by himself on a park bench.
'Have a chip,' I said.
'I'm full,' he said.
I don't know what made me do it
but I sat down next to him.
'Best chips you can get,' I said.
'Yea.'
Then he smiled a real big smile.
'What do they call you?' he asked.
'They call me lots of things,' I said.
'But my name's Mollie.'

We chattered about this and that
and walked along Duckworth Way together.
Only it should have been called 'Heaven's Way'
for that's where I was.
I just knew Gary was for me.
We came to a big wire fence.
'I'm in here,' he said.
'What?'

'Duckworth's Scrap Yard. I work here.'
He slipped through a gap in the wire fence.
Then he went past a pile of smashed up
old cars and was gone.

3

Gary's Secret

It was football training night.
Our coach, Amy, put out a line of cones.
We had to kick the ball around each cone.
You only had two kicks
to get the ball around each cone.
To start with I did it well. Then I lost it.
I knocked over a load of the cones.
The ball went all over the place.
I really lost my cool.
I kicked the ball over the fence.
I kicked over a cone.

'Red card, Mollie,' shouted Amy.
'If you play like that in the cup replay
you'll get sent off.'
'Stuff it,' I said.
'Easy Mollie.'
'No. I've had enough tonight.'
I went into the changing rooms and changed.
In less than five minutes
I was down the scrap yard.
That was really where I wanted to be.
I wanted to be with Gary.
He was just finishing work.

'Do you fancy watching a video?' I asked him.
'Yea.'
We went to the video shop.
'What about *Zombie 2*?' I asked him.
'Seen it.'
'*Brain Dead 4*?'
'I heard it was boring.'
'*Dead Hand 5*?'
'No.'
'No?'

'No. I've a better idea. Come on.'
He pulled me out of the shop.
'Where are we going?'
He didn't answer.
'Come on Gary where are we going?'
'It's a surprise.
You'll see when we get there,' he said.

We walked right across town.
We walked fast. It was miles.
We started to climb up a big hill.
Here there was no busy town traffic,
just a long line of little gardens.

'These are allotments where old folk
grow stuff,' said Gary.
'And here is what I wanted you to see.'
He pointed to an ugly old wooden shed.
'This?' I asked.
'We walked all this way to see this?'
'Listen,' he said and he held my hand
really tight.
'I can't hear anything.'
'Really listen,' he said.

I tried again. I could hear a faint noise.
It was coming from the shed.
'It's pigeons,' he said.
'I love pigeons. I race them.
They can fly thousands and thousands of miles.'

We went round the back of the shed.
There were gaps in the shed
so the pigeons could fly in and out.
He took a pigeon and held it in one hand.
The pigeon made a gentle cooing sound
as he stroked its grey feathers.
'This is Beauty. She's my special bird.
She wins loads of races.'
'I don't bring people up here,' he said.
'Somebody once smashed up the shed.
They killed some of my best birds.
You can't be too careful.
I keep the pigeons secret from all my mates.'

'I've got a secret too,' I said.
'I play football in a girl's team.
We've got a big cup match on Saturday.
It's a replay. Will you come to see me play?'

4

The Replay

Saturday came. But there was no Gary.
He said he'd come to see me play
yet he was nowhere to be seen.
I tried to forget about him
and think about the match.

The replay was on Rovers' ground
which was famous for being on a slope.
We kicked downhill in the first half.

'We need two goals before half-time.
At least two,' said Amy.
'Second half will be all uphill for us.
They are bound to score
when they kick downhill.'
Then she looked at me.
'Mollie … stay calm and in control.
Remember we don't want any red cards.'

We ran out on to the pitch to the sound of boos.
Their fans were going to give us a hard time.
'Concentrate,' shouted Amy from the touchline.

We began badly. The slope was beating us.
Every pass went wide. Every kick was too long.
We gave the ball away or kicked it miles
over the touchline. Their fans booed.
'They can't kick,' shouted one of the crowd.
'They can't pass,' shouted another.
'They can't play,' shouted a third.
'Don't blast it, City,' shouted Amy.
'Short sharp passes. That's what we need.'

Samita gave me a good pass.
I ran towards the ball.
But the slope carried it away from me.
I ran faster. The ball trickled
out of play for their throw in.
Jeers sounded from the crowd.
'PATHETIC,' they shouted.

I could feel myself going red in the face.
We had to do something about this.
They took the throw in and caught us asleep.
Now it was their chance to attack.
Uphill they ran, with the ball at their feet.
Quick one two passes carried them on.
This was looking dangerous.
Their number nine had the ball.
She was just ahead of me.
She saw me, stopped and turned her back on me.
She looked towards the centre of the pitch
'Yes,' shouted another Rovers' player.
'Give me the ball. Yes.' she shouted.
'No. No.' I said to myself
as I ran at the number nine.

I lost control. I kicked her from behind.
She fell to the ground in a heap.
The crowd booed loudly.
The ref blew her whistle.
'OFF, OFF, OFF,' shouted the crowd.
The ref stared at me.
Then she pointed her finger.
'Come here,' she said.
I walked slowly towards her.
She pulled a card out of her pocket.

'SEND HER OFF, SEND HER OFF,'
screamed the crowd.
I knew it would be red. It had to be.
I could see Amy out on the touchline
with her head in her hands.
The card was out. It was … YELLOW.

The crowd booed even louder.
The ref blew her whistle for half-time.
Amy came towards me.
'Don't you ever do that again, Mollie,'
she said.
'You're lucky to still be playing.
So whatever is bugging you forget it.
We need all your skill this half.
We needed to have hit
the back of the net by now.
This half will be really hard for us.'

It was a battle. Now they had the slope.
They came at us in one big wave.
We fell back in defence.
Now at last we began to play like one team.

We defended hard. We tackled and kicked.
We supported each other.
Sometimes they did break through
or tried a shot at goal.
Then Chalky, our goalie, had it covered.
She jumped and leapt. She caught the ball
or punched it out. She was brilliant.
'Well played. Well done,'
shouted Amy from the touchline.
Now we were getting really tired.
Soon they must score,
but the end of the match was close.

'Hang in there,' shouted Amy.
'It's not long before the final whistle.'
I had the ball. I ran forward a few paces.
I looked towards the touchline.
I just wanted to kick the ball
as hard as I could.
If I could kick it out of play
we could have a bit of a rest.
If I could kick it over the fence
we could have an even longer rest.

It would take them ages to get the ball back.
I ran forward a few paces more
and gave the ball the hardest kick I could.
It flew high up in the air.
A wind had got up and it carried the ball
away from the fence.
'Stuff it,' I said to myself.
The ball was still high up in the air.
It swirled round and round.
Down it came and bounced
in the middle of the pitch.
Now some of the Rovers players
could see the danger.
'Look out,' they shouted at their goalie.
It was too late. The ball bounced again.
It went right over the goalie's head
and into the back of their net.
We had won the match 1–0.

5

All Mixed Up

I went to the scrap yard.
I looked round all the rusty cars.
'Gary ... Gary,' I shouted.
But Gary wasn't there.
There was only one place he could be.
I ran most of the way. Past busy shops.
Along crowded pavements.
On and on until I came
to the line of little gardens.
He was sitting by the shed
with his pigeon Beauty in his hands.

'Where were you?' I said.

He said nothing. He just stroked the pigeon.

'Come on answer,' I said.

'I came all this way to see you.

You might say something.'

'Don't shout.

You'll frighten the pigeon,' he said quietly.

I looked at the pigeon.

It had a hard orange eye with a black dot
in the middle. It never blinked.

It looked up at me with that hard eye.

That pigeon made me even more angry.

'Stuff the pigeon,' I said.

Then I was crying and sad
and angry and all mixed up.

It was ages before I could speak.

'You said you'd come to the match,' I said.

'I hate football,' he said.

'You didn't tell me that.'

'I didn't want to upset you,' he said.

'You could have told me.
I was expecting to see you at the match.'
'I hate football,' he said again.
'You could have come just for me.
I walked all this way to see you.
Won't you do something for me.
Please Gary come to the cup final.
Please?'

6

The Final

I walked away from the pigeon shed
and I walked away from Gary.
I didn't know if I'd see him again.
I didn't know if I cared. I was so mixed up.
Was it football or Gary? Did I have to choose?
Why couldn't I have both?

There were just a few days before the final.
On day one Amy had us doing extra training.
We had to go on a four-mile run. It was agony.
On day two we met a reporter
from the local paper.
He asked us loads of questions:
'What's so great about football?'
'What's it like playing in a girls' team?'
'Do you think women footballers
will ever be as good as men?'
On day three we had our picture in the paper.
It had a bit written about each of us
including me:

'Gollie Miss Mollie.
Will headstrong Mollie cool it for the final?'

What a cheek!
On day four we were given a brand new strip
sponsored by the local paper.
This was going to be a week to remember.
Day five meant taking things easy
because day six was match day.

We got to the ground early
and into the changing rooms.
Everyone had cards wishing them good luck.
I looked through mine hoping I might see one
from pigeon man. No such luck.

Then we went on to the pitch.
It was a perfect pitch.
It was so green and flat.
'Good for making neat passes,' said Amy.
'This is the biggest match
we have played so far.
Try to enjoy it whatever the result.
Win or lose. I am proud of you all.'

At three o'clock we ran out of the tunnel
and into the game.
I sprinted onto the pitch and tried
to keep calm. But my feet were like jelly.
My heart was thumping fast.
I had almost reached our goal
when a loud voice shouted from the crowd,
'MOLLIE'.

I looked up. It was him.
Gary had come to the match.
He was there for me.
Now I felt like that pigeon flying in space.
Whatever the result of the match
I wouldn't return to earth for ninety minutes.
After that I'd go out with Gary
and we wouldn't just be eating chips.